THEORY MUSIC MADE EASY

GRADE 1

Lina Ng

© RHYTHM MP SDN. BHD.1991

Published By
RHYTHM MP SDN. BHD.
1947, Lorong IKS Bukit Minyak 2,
Taman IKS Bukit Minyak, 14100 Simpang Ampat,
Penang, Malaysia.
Tel: +60 4 5050246 (Direct Line), +60 4 5073690 (Hunting Line)
Fax: +60 4 5050691
E-mail: rhythmmp@mphsb.com
Website: www.rhythmmp.com

ISBN 967-985-293-8
Order No.: MPT-3003-01

Rhythm MP

CONTENTS

NAME	NOTE CHART	COUNTS
Semibreve	𝄾	4
Minim	♩ ♩	2
Crotchet	♩ ♩ ♩ ♩	1
Quaver	♪ ♪ ♫ ♫ ♫	1/2

1. Fill in the time values.

(a)   𝅝   ♩   ♩   ♪   𝅝   ♩   ♪   ♩

     4

(b)   ♪   ♩   ♪   𝅝   ♩   𝅝   ♩   ♩

2. Name the notes.

A _____

C _____

E _____

B _____

D _____

F _____

3. Fill in the blanks with the correct number. $\boxed{2}\boxed{4}\boxed{8}$

(a) 𝅝 = ... 𝅗𝅥

(b) 𝅝 = ... 𝅘𝅥

(c) 𝅝 = ... 𝅘𝅥𝅮

(d) 𝅗𝅥 = ... 𝅘𝅥

(e) 𝅗𝅥 = ... 𝅘𝅥𝅮

(f) 𝅘𝅥 = ... 𝅘𝅥𝅮

4. Bunny is looking for crabs. Colour the crabs according to the time values.

4 counts = red	2 counts = yellow	1 count = green

↑	︶ bar	↑	↑
time signature		bar-line	double bar-line

Simple Duple	$\frac{2}{4}$	=	2 ♩	=	2 crotchet beats in a bar
Simple Triple	$\frac{3}{4}$	=	3 ♩	=	3 crotchet beats in a bar
Simple Quadruple	$\frac{4}{4}$	=	4 ♩	=	4 crotchet beats in a bar

$\frac{4}{4}$ time can also be represented by the symbol **C** which means common time.
The top number tells how many beats in a bar.
The bottom number tells the kind of note used to represent the beat.

1. First write the counts, then prefix the correct time signature.

2. Add bar-lines to the following.

3. Add a note to complete each bar.

4. Prefix the time signatures.

(a)

(b)

(c)

(d) (e) (f)

1. Under each note, write its time name. (e.g. 1/2, 1, etc.)

....

2. Name the notes. (e.g. crotchet, etc.)

....

3. Add the correct time signature to each of the following.

4. Add a note to complete each bar.

(a)

(b)

5. Add bar-lines to the following.

(a)

(b)

A stave (staff) consists of 5 **Ledger Lines**.

Short ledger lines may be added to indicate notes above or below the stave.

Position of Middle C

Notes in the *Treble Clef*.

C   D   E   F   G   A   B   C   D   E   F   G

1. Copy the treble clef.

2. Name the notes.

3. Write the notes.

F - space   D - line   E - space   G - line   C - line

F - line   B - line   D - space   A - space   G - space

Notes in the *Bass Clef*.

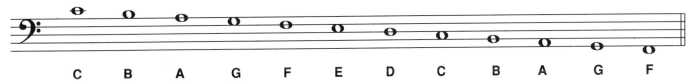

C	B	A	G	F	E	D	C	B	A	G	F

4. **Copy the bass clef.**

5. **Name the notes.**

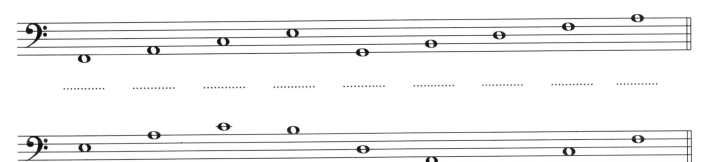

6. **Prefix the correct clef before each note.**

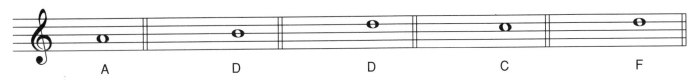

A   D   D   C   F

B   G   E   B   G

E   C   A   F   B

7. Match the notes to the letter names.

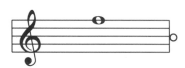

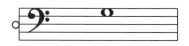

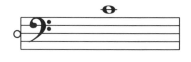
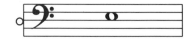
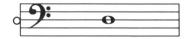

NAME	NOTE CHART	COUNTS
Crotchet		1
Quaver		1/2
Semiquaver		1/4

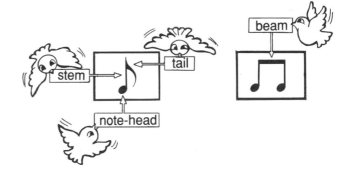

1. Mark true ✓ or false ✗ .

(a) ♩ = 4 ✗

(b) ♩ = 8 ✗

(c) 𝅝 = 16

(d) ♪ = 3 ✗

(e) ♩ = 5 ✗

(f) 𝅝 = 32 ✗

2. Rewrite the following joining the quavers and semiquavers.

(a)

(c)

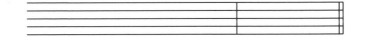

(b)

(d)

1. Name the following.

a   b   c   d   e   f

a = ...   d = ...

b = ...   e = ...

c = ...   f = ...

2. Write the following notes as *Semibreves*.

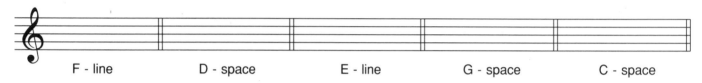

F - line   D - space   E - line   G - space   C - space

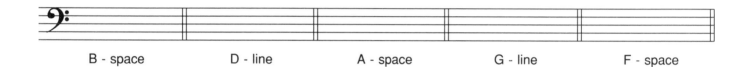

B - space   D - line   A - space   G - line   F - space

3. Rewrite the following joining the notes where necessary.

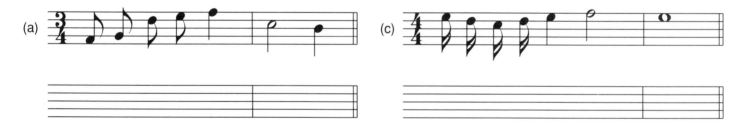

(a)   (c)

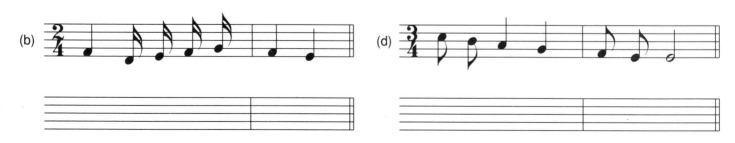

(b)   (d)

NAME	NOTE	REST	COUNTS
Semibreve	𝅝	▬	4
Minim	𝅗𝅥	▬	2
Crotchet	𝅘𝅥	𝄽	1
Quaver	𝅘𝅥𝅮	𝄾	1/2
Semiquaver	𝅘𝅥𝅯	𝄿	1/4

 A bar rest is used to fill an empty bar of $\frac{2}{4}$, $\frac{3}{4}$, $\frac{4}{4}$ time.

1. Insert a rest at each of the places marked * .

(a)

(b)

(c)

2. Insert a rest at each of the places marked * .

(a)

(b)

Grade 1

A tie joins notes of the same sound.

1. **Write down the number of *Crotchet* beats.**

(a) 𝅝 = **4**

(b) 𝅗𝅥 = ...

(c) 𝅘𝅥 = ...

(d) 𝅘𝅥𝅮 = ...

(e) 𝅘𝅥𝅯 = ...

2. **First, join notes of the same sound with a tie. Then, write the number of *Crotchet* beats made by the tie.**

(a)

........**3**....... beats

(b)

.... beats

(c)

.... beats

(d)

.... beats

(e)

.... beats

(f)

.... beats

3. **Mark true ✓ or false ✗.**

(a) 𝅗𝅥 ⌣ 𝅘𝅥𝅯 = 2¼ beats ⬭

(b) 𝅘𝅥 ⌣ 𝅘𝅥𝅮 = 1½ beats ⬭

(c) 𝅗𝅥 ⌣ 𝅗𝅥. = 4½ beats ⬭

(d) 𝅗𝅥. ⌣ 𝅘𝅥 = 4 beats ⬭

(e) 𝅘𝅥 ⌣ 𝅘𝅥𝅯 = 1¼ beats ⬭

(f) 𝅗𝅥 ⌣ 𝅘𝅥𝅮 = 2¼ beats ⬭

Dotted Minim	𝅗𝅥.	=	𝅗𝅥	+	♩	=	♩ ♩ ♩
Dotted Crotchet	♩.	=	♩	+	♪	=	♪ ♪ ♪
Dotted Quaver	♪.	=	♪	+	♬	=	♬ ♬ ♬

1. Fill in the blanks with the correct number. | 1½ | 3 | 6 | 12 |

(a) 𝅗𝅥. = ... 𝅗𝅥

(b) 𝅗𝅥. = ... ♩

(c) 𝅗𝅥. = ... ♪

(d) 𝅗𝅥. = ... ♬

(e) ♩. = ... ♩

(f) ♩. = ... ♪

(g) ♩. = ... ♪

(h) ♪. = ... ♬

2. Add dots where necessary to make complete bars.

(a)

(b)

(c)

3. Add bar-lines to the following.

(a)

(b)

1. Under each of the following, write its time name. (e.g. 1, 1/2, etc.)

....

2. Next to each of the following, write a note that has the same time value.

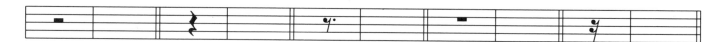

3. Mark true ✓ or false ✗ .

(a) — = — ◯   (e) — = — ◯

(b) — = — ◯   (f) — = — ◯

(c) — = — ◯   (g) — = — ◯

(d) — = — ◯   (h) — = — ◯

4. Add one rest at each of the places marked ✳ to make the bars complete.

♯ sharp	=	raises a note 1 semitone in pitch
♭ flat	=	lowers a note 1 semitone in pitch
♮ natural	=	restores a note to its original pitch

An accidental against a note affects every later appearance of that note at the same pitch in the bar.

If the note F at a different pitch is to be sharpened, it must be shown by another sharp.

1. Put a sharp (♯) before every note and name the notes.

C sharp

2. Put a flat (♭) before every note and name the notes.

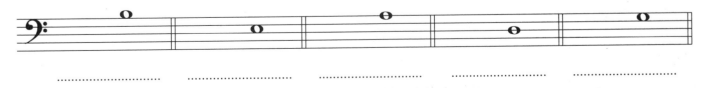

Grade 1

3. Put a natural (♮) before every note and name the notes.

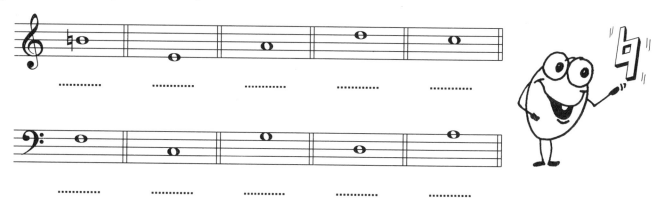

....

....

4. Write the required notes.

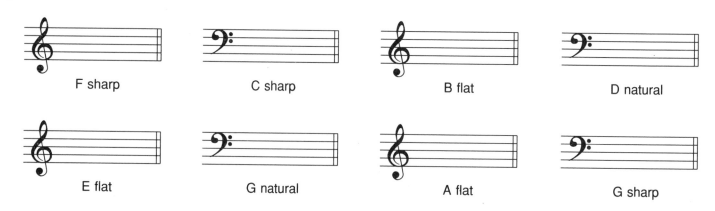

F sharp   C sharp   B flat   D natural

E flat   G natural   A flat   G sharp

5. Name the numbered notes.

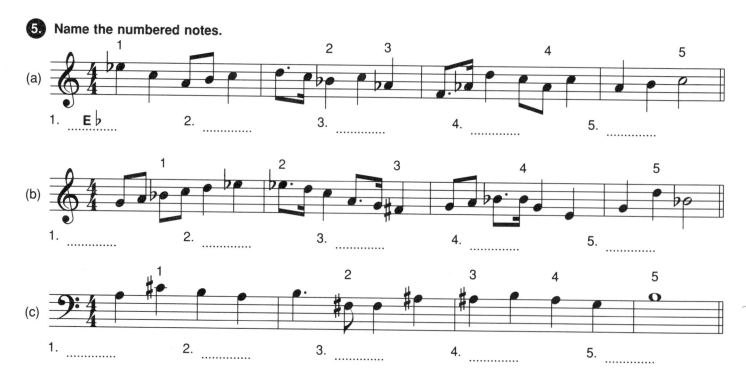

(a)

1. **E♭**   2. ....   3. ....   4. ....   5. ....

(b)

1. ....   2. ....   3. ....   4. ....   5. ....

(c)

1. ....   2. ....   3. ....   4. ....   5. ....

Grade 1

Cancelling an accidental

An accidental lasts until the end of the bar.

(a)

1. B♭   2. B♭

To change the note back to B♮, a ♮ sign is added.

(b)

1. B♭   2. B♮

(c)

1. B♭   2. B♮

Other examples.

(d)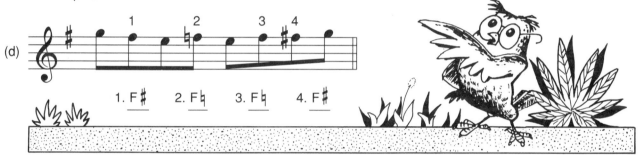

1. F♯   2. F♮   3. F♮   4. F♯

6. **Before each of the notes marked *, add an accidental required to cancel the previous accidental.**

(a)

(e)

(b)

(f)

(c)

(g)

(d)

(h)

Semitones and Tones

1. Complete the diagram.

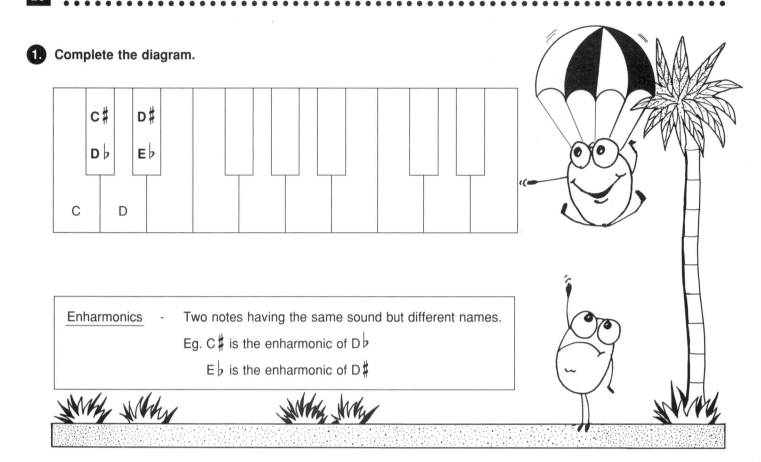

Enharmonics — Two notes having the same sound but different names.

Eg. C♯ is the enharmonic of D♭

E♭ is the enharmonic of D♯

2. Tick (✓) the higher note of each pair.

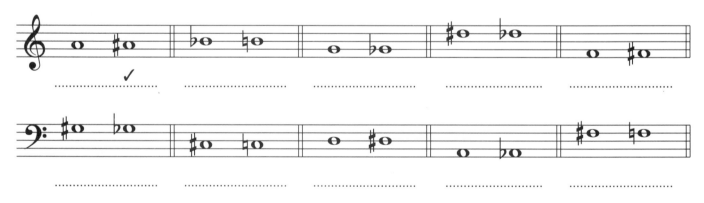

3. Tick (✓) the lower note of each pair.

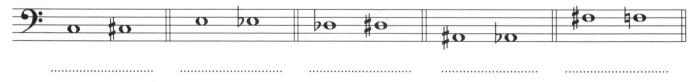

SEMITONE - The distance in pitch between a note and its nearest neighbour.

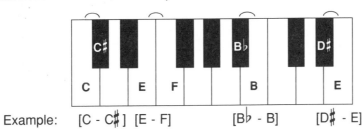

Example: [C - C♯] [E - F]   [B♭ - B]   [D♯ - E]

4. Write notes one semitone higher.

5. Write notes one semitone lower.

6. Add an accidental (♯, ♭, ♮) to the 2nd note to make it a semitone higher than the 1st.
If no accidental is needed, put a tick (✓).

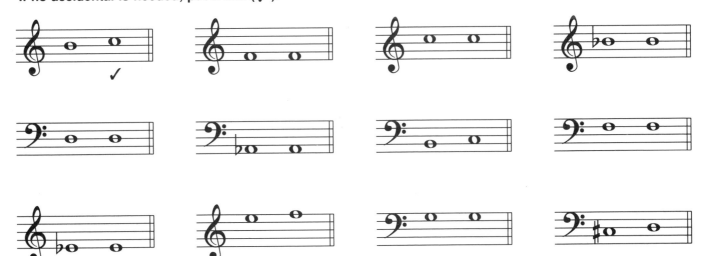

TONE - An interval of 2 semitones.

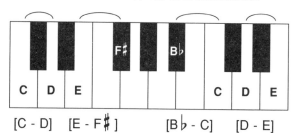

Example: [C - D] [E - F♯] [B♭ - C] [D - E]

7. Write notes one tone higher.

8. Write notes one tone lower.

9. Draw a bracket (⌐‾‾‾¬) over each pair of notes which make a tone.

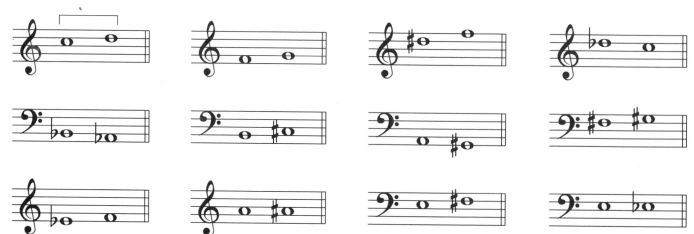

G major	- F♯
D major	- F♯, C♯
F major	- B♭
C major	- no sharps and flats

1. **Copy the following.**

G major

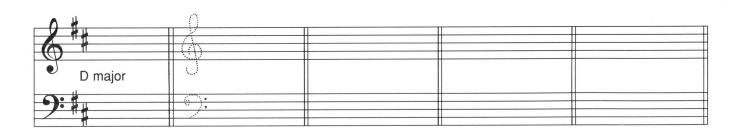

D major

F major

2. **Name the major keys which have the following key signatures.**

Key ....

Key ....

Key ....

Key ....

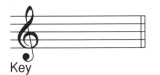

Key ....

Key ....

Key ....

Key ....

3. Name the keys, then rewrite the passages using key signatures instead of accidentals.

(a)  Key ....

(b) Key ....

(c) Key ....

(d) Key ....

(e) Key ....

(f) Key ....

4. Insert sharps (♯) or flats (♭) to form the keys.

(a)

D major

(b)

G major

(c)

F major

(d)

D major

(e)

G major

(f)

F major

(g)

D major

Revision 4 ✍

1. Write the following notes as *Semibreves*.

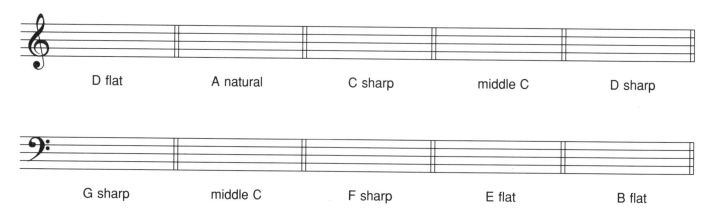

D flat   A natural   C sharp   middle C   D sharp

G sharp   middle C   F sharp   E flat   B flat

2. Under each of the following notes write its letter name.

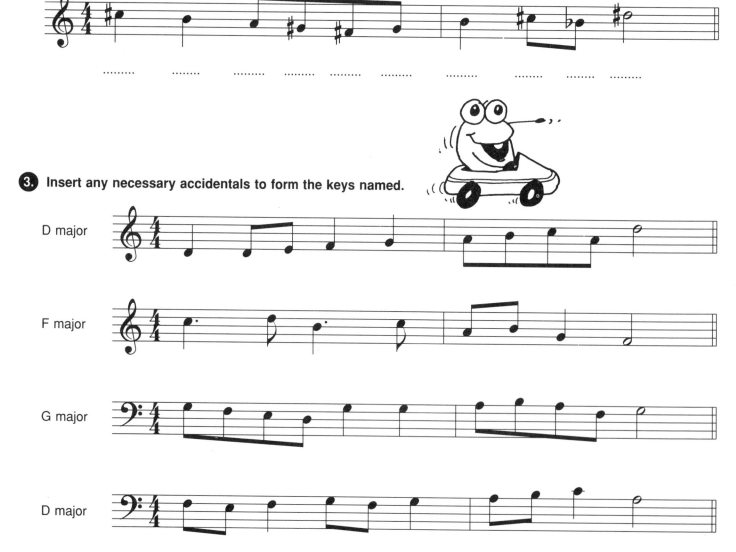

3. Insert any necessary accidentals to form the keys named.

D major

F major

G major

D major

Ascending scales.

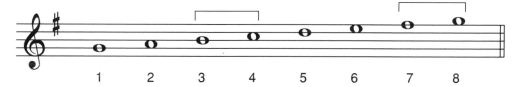

Eg. G major, with key signature

In a major scale, semitones occur on the 3 - 4 and 7 - 8 notes.

1. **Write scales with key signatures, ascending. Bracket (⌐‾‾‾⌐) the semitones.**

F major

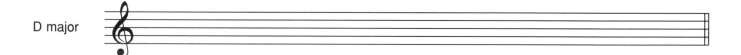

D major

G major

Eg. G major, without key signature

2. **Write scales without key signatures, ascending. Bracket (⌐‾‾‾⌐) the semitones.**

F major

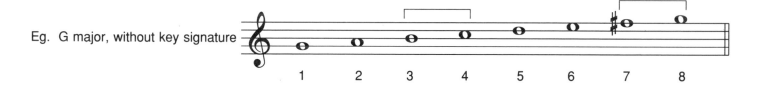

D major

G major

Descending scales

Eg. G major, with key signature

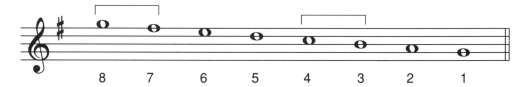

8 7 6 5 4 3 2 1

3. Write scales with key signatures, descending. Bracket ( ) semitones.

F major

D major

G major

Eg. G major without key signature

4. Write scales without key signatures, descending. Bracket ( ) semitones.

F major

D major

G major

5. Add accidentals before the notes to form the scales named. Then, mark semitones with ⬜.

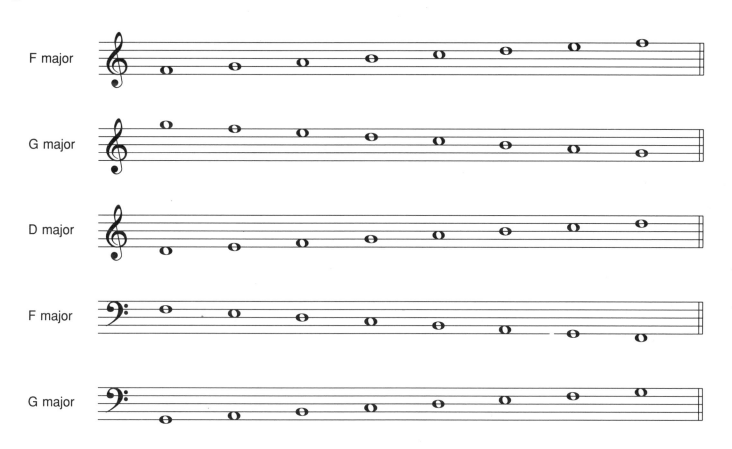

F major

G major

D major

F major

G major

6. Add the clefs and key signatures to make the scales named.

F major

D major

G major

F major

7. **Write scales as instructed.**

(a) Write a treble clef and then the key signature of F major and the scale ascending. Use the given rhythm.

(b) Write a bass clef and then the scale of C major descending. Use the given rhythm. Bracket (⌐‾‾⌐)the semitones.

(c) Write without key signature the scale of D major ascending, using *Semibreves*.
Mark each semitone with a bracket (⌐‾‾⌐).

(d) Write the major scale belonging to the given key signature, descending. Mark each semitone with a bracket (⌐‾‾⌐).

(e) Write without key signature the major scale going up on the given key-note.

(f) Write with the correct key signature in the bass clef the scale of D major going down. Use the given rhythm.

(g) Write in the treble clef the scale of C major going up. Bracket (⌐‾‾⌐) each semitone. Use the given rhythm.

| Interval | - The distance in pitch between 2 different notes. |

| Melodic Interval | - The 2 notes are played one after another. |

| Harmonic Interval | - The 2 notes are played together. |

> Key-note - The note on which a scale begins.
> Eg. In C major, the key-note is C
> In G major, the key-note is G

The number of degrees is the number of the interval.

| 2nd = second | 4th = fourth | 6th = sixth | 8th = eighth |
| 3rd = third | 5th = fifth | 7th = seventh | 8ve = octave |

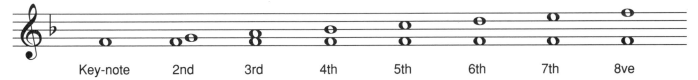

| Key-note | 2nd | 3rd | 4th | 5th | 6th | 7th | 8ve |

1. Write the number of the intervals. (2nd, 3rd, 4th, 5th, etc.)

Melodic Intervals

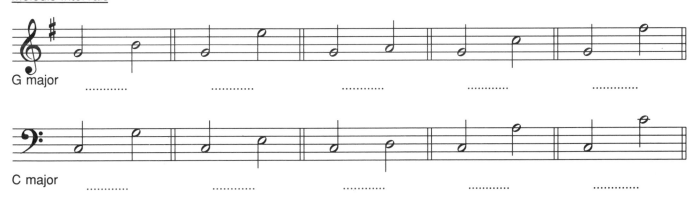

G major

C major

Harmonic Intervals

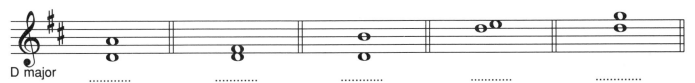

D major

F major

2. Above each note, add a *Semibreve* to make the named interval.

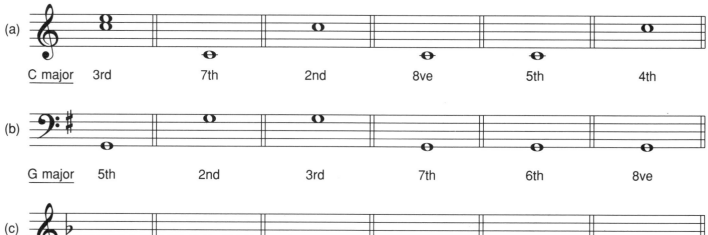

C major 3rd · 7th · 2nd · 8ve · 5th · 4th

G major 5th · 2nd · 3rd · 7th · 6th · 8ve

F major 4th · 7th · 6th · 2nd · 5th · 3rd

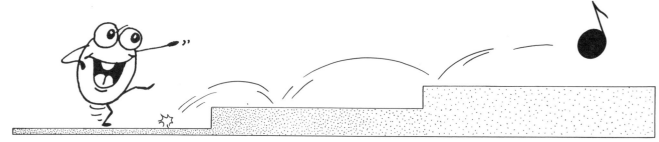

3. Write the number of the intervals marked ⌐‾‾⌐. (2nd, 3rd, 4th, etc.)

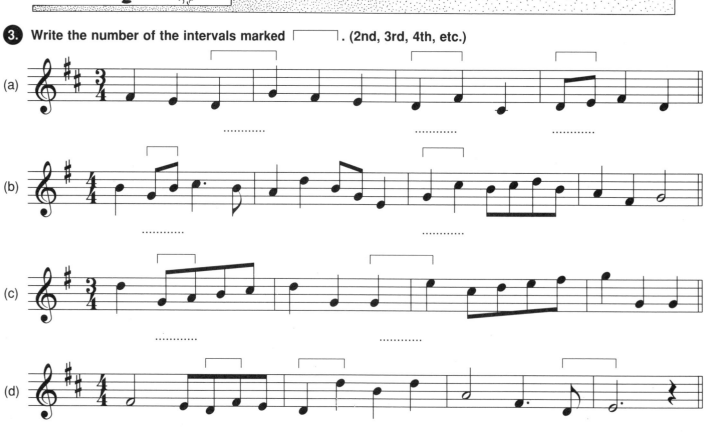

(a) ....

(b) ....

(c) ....

(d) ....

Grade 1

1. Copy the tonic triads with key signatures.

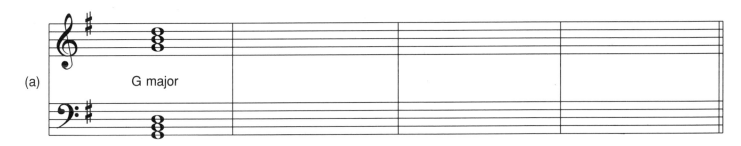

(a) G major

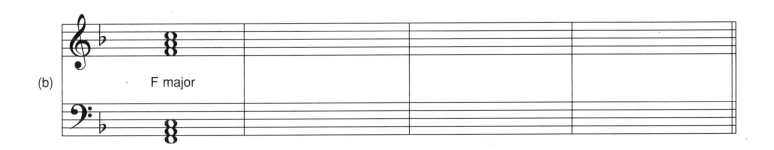

(b) F major

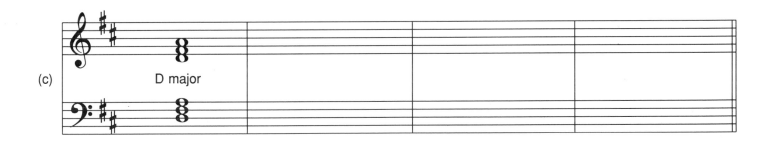

(c) D major

2. Copy the tonic triads without key signatures.

(a) D major

(b) C major

3. **Answer the questions below.**

(a) How many notes form a triad ?

    A. 2   B. 3   C. 4

(b) Which notes of a major scale are used to form a tonic triad ?

    A. 1, 3, 5   B. 2, 4, 6   C. 3, 5, 7

(c) Circle the notes used to form the tonic triads named.

C major - Ⓒ   D   Ⓔ   F   Ⓖ   A   B   C

D major - D   E   F♯   G   A   B   C♯   D

F major - F   G   A   B♭   C   D   E   F

G major - G   A   B   C   D   E   F♯   G

4. **Name the tonic triads indicated by the dots on the keyboard.**

A

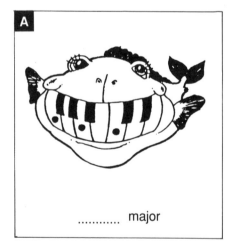

.... major

C

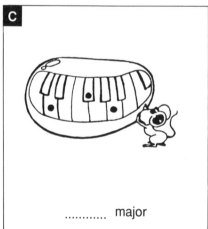

.... major

E

.... major

B

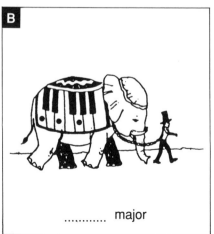

.... major

D

.... major

F

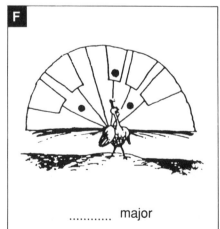

.... major

5. Name the keys of the tonic triads.

Key ....

Key ....

6. Write tonic triads with key signatures.

D major   G major   F major   C major

C major   D major   G major   F major

7. Write tonic triads without key signatures.

F major   D major   G major   C major

C major   G major   D major   F major

1. Name the key of each of the following . Draw ⌐‾‾⌐ over one pair of notes making a semitone, in each case.

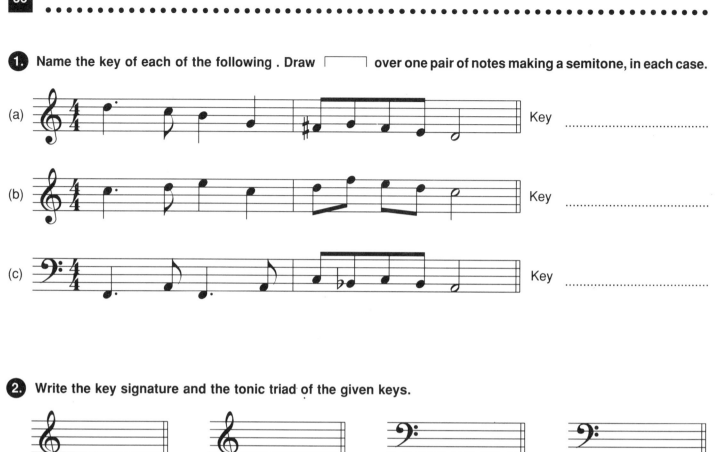

(a) Key ....

(b) Key ....

(c) Key ....

2. Write the key signature and the tonic triad of the given keys.

F major   G major   D major   C major

3. Write the clef and then the named tonic triad, without key signature, starting on the key-note given.

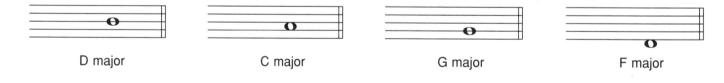

D major   C major   G major   F major

4. Add the correct clefs and any accidentals to make the scales named. Do not use a key signature.

(a) D major

(b) F major

Correct Grouping of Notes

1. Rewrite the following using beams and dots.

(a)

(b)

(c)

(f) three-four time

(g) four-four time

(h) four-four time

(i) four-four time

When writing an answering rhythm, remember to end it with a long note (o 𝅝. 𝅗𝅥 or 𝅘𝅥).

Do not end with a ♪ or 𝅘𝅥𝅮 as the rhythm may seem unfinished.

2. Add an answering two-bar rhythm to each of the following.

(a)

(b)

(c)

(d)

(e)

(f)

(g)

(h)

(i)

(j)

(k)

(l)

(m)

(n)

(o)

Italian Terms and Signs (Grade 1)

Terms

1. *forte (f)*   - loud
   mezzo forte (mf)   - moderately loud
   fortissimo (ff)   - very loud

2. *piano (p)*   - soft
   mezzo piano (mp)   - moderately soft
   pianissimo (pp)   - very soft

3. *crescendo (cresc.)*   - getting louder
   decrescendo   - getting softer
   diminuendo (dim.)   - getting softer

4. *allegro*   - lively, fast
   allegretto   - slightly slower than *allegro*

5. *lento*   - slow
   adagio   - slow

6. *accelerando (accel.)*   - getting faster
   rallentando (rall.)   - getting slower
   ritardando (ritard.)   - getting slower
   ritenuto (rit.)   - hold back (slower at once)
   andante   - at a moderate pace (walking speed)

7. *Da Capo (D.C.)*   - from the beginning
   Fine   - the end
   Da Capo al Fine   - from the beginning to the end
   Dal Segno (D.S.)   - from the sign 𝄋

8. *cantabile*   - in a singing style
   staccato   - short, detached
   legato   - smoothly
   moderato   - moderately
   mezzo   - half
   poco   - a little
   tempo   - the speed of the music
   a tempo   - resume the normal speed

Signs

1. ⌒ - pause

2. > - accent

3. ⌢ - tie

4. ⌢ - slur

5. - staccato

6. ‖: :‖ - repeat sign

7. < - getting louder

8. > - getting softer

9. **M.M.** ♩ = **88** - 88 crotchet beats in a minute (**M.M.** - Maelzel's Metronome)

10. <> - getting louder then softer

11. *8ᵛᵃ* - ottava (octave)

    8ᵛᵃ ⌐ - perform an octave higher

    8ᵛᵃ ⌐ - perform an octave lower

12. - slur or phrase (play smoothly)

1. Give the meaning of these Italian terms

a tempo	-
accelerando	-
adagio	-
allegretto	-
allegro	-
andante	-
cantabile	-
crescendo	-
da capo	-
dal segno	-
decrescendo	-
diminuendo	-
fine	-
forte	-
fortissimo	-
legato	-
lento	-
mezzo	-
mezzo forte	-
mezzo piano	-
moderato	-
piano	-
pianissimo	-
poco	-
rallentando	-
ritardando	-
ritenuto	-
staccato	-
tempo	-

2. **Write out these abbreviations in full.**

f -

p -

mf -

mp -

ff -

pp -

cresc. -

dim. -

accel. -

rall. -

ritard. -

rit. -

D.C. -

D.S. -

3. **Write the signs for the following.**

getting louder -

getting softer -

repeat sign -

pause -

accent -

staccato dots -

tie -

play an octave higher -

play an octave lower -

1. **Look at the melody below, then answer the questions.**

Allegro

Chopin, Mazurka Op.68 No.3

1. What does **Allegro** mean ? ....

2. What key is the melody in ? ....

3. What is the time signature ? ....

4. How many crotchet beats are there in a bar ? ....

5. How many times does the note B♭ appear ? ....

6. How many times is this rhythm ♪. ♪ ♩ ♩ used ? ....

    How many times is this rhythm ♪. ♪ ♩ used ? ....

7. What is the name of the highest note used ? ....

    What is the name of the lowest note used ? ....

8. What is the value of the shortest note ? ....

9. What is *f* short for ? ....

    What does it mean ? ....

10. What degree of the scale is the last note in the melody ?   (2nd,   3rd,   4th,   5th)

11. Name 2 pairs of notes which are a semitone apart. (....... — ....) and (....... — ....)

12. Copy out the first 2 bars of the melody.

2. Look at the melody below and answer the questions.

1. What does $\quad$ = 80 stand for ? ....

2. Name the key of the melody. ....

3. What is the time signature ? ....

4. Another way to write the time signature is

5. Write a rest equivalent to the last note of the melody.

6. How many times does the key-note appear ? ....

7. How many times is this rhythm  used? ....

8. What is the name of the shortest note used ? ....

9. Give the meaning of these terms and signs.

    mf $\quad$ - .... $\qquad$ *dim.* - ....

    $\diagup$ - .... $\qquad$ *p* - ....

10. What is the name of the dot $\quad$ ....

    What does it mean ? ....

11. Name a pair of notes which are a semitone apart. (....... — ....)

12. Copy out the last 2 bars of the melody. Put in the clef, key signature and time signature.

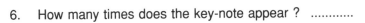

Grade 1

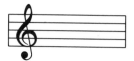

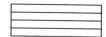

3. **Look at the melody below and answer the questions.**

1. What is the key of the melody ? ....

    Name the key signature. ....

2. What is the time signature ? ....

    What does it mean ? ....

3. What are the curved lines over the melody called ? ....

    How should they be played ? ....

4. How many bars are there in this melody ? ....

5. On which degree of the scale does the melody begin on ? (1st, 2nd, 3rd, 4th) ....

    On which degree of the scale does the melody end on ? (1st, 2nd, 3rd, 4th) ....

6. Which bars do not contain the key-note ? Bars .... , ... , ...

7. What does **Allegretto** mean ? ....

8. What does ⌢ mean ? ....

9. Name the notes in bar 4. ....

10. Write the tonic triad of this melody, with key signature.

11. Write a rest equivalent to the 1st note of the 4th bar.

12. Copy out the first 2 bars of the melody.

```
A  C  C  E  L  E  R  A  N  D  O
L  O  R  F  E  N  D  N  T  I  N
L  A  E  D  N  I  S  D  O  M  E
E  A  S  C  T  O  N  A  S  I  P
G  O  C  A  O  P  A  N  E  N  O
R  F  E  C  U  T  E  T  R  U  C
O  O  N  E  F  I  N  E  N  E  O
P  R  D  I  M  O  L  S  I  N  E
U  T  O  L  E  A  D  U  M  D  S
L  E  S  T  A  C  C  A  T  O  P
```

To find out the Italian Terms hidden in this maze, answer the questions below.

1. On a clear road, I drive *gradually faster*. _ _ _ _ _ _ _ _ _ _ _

2. The clown danced very *lively and fast*. _ _ _ _ _ _ _ _ _

3. She always walks at a *moderate speed*. _ _ _ _ _ _ _ _

4. The teacher is angry because the pupils are talking *louder and louder*. _ _ _ _ _ _ _ _ _ _ _

5. When the battery is running out, the radio becomes *softer and softer*. _ _ _ _ _ _ _ _ _ _ _ _

6. When I'm angry I speak *loudly*. _ _ _ _ _ _

7. The old lady walks *slowly*. _ _ _ _ _ _

8. When I'm not hungry, I eat only *a little*. _ _ _ _ _

9. I am very *short and detached*. _ _ _ _ _ _ _ _

10. This is *the end*. _ _ _ _ _

Crossword Puzzle (Game)

Across

1. Another name for the F clef is __ __ __ __ .

2. You join two quaver notes with a __ __ __ __ .

3. __ __ __ __ __ __ __ __ __ means in a singing style.

4. Two semitones is equal to a __ __ __ __ .

5. The line that joins two notes of the same pitch is called a __ __ __ .

6. A crotchet consists of a note-head and a __ __ __ __ .

7. A tonic triad consists of __ __ __ __ __ notes.

Down

4. The __ __ __ __ __ __ clef is usually meant for the right hand.

6. A __ __ __ __ __ raises the pitch of a note by one semitone.

8. A __ __ __ __ __ lasts as long as two crotchets.

9. There are four __ __ __ __ __ __ __ __ __ __ __ in a crotchet.

10. __ __ __ __ __ __ is the Italian word for slow.

11. Another name for key-note is __ __ __ __ __ .

12. > is an __ __ __ __ __ __ __ .

13. The distance in pitch between two different notes is called an __ __ __ __ __ __ __ __ __ .

14. F sharp is the __ __ __ - signature of G major.